This b

Other Titles of Interest

THE ART OF SOLDERING

by

R. BREWSTER

BERNARD BABANI (publishing) LTD
THE GRAMPIANS
SHEPHERDS BUSH ROAD
LONDON W6 7NF
ENGLAND

Please Note

Although every care has been taken with the production of this book to ensure that any projects, designs, modifications and/or programs etc. contained herewith, operate in a correct and safe manner and also that all components specified are normally available in Great Britain, the Publishers and Author do not accept responsibility in any way for the failure, including fault in design, of any project, design, modification or program to work correctly or to cause damage to any other equipment that it may be connected to or used in conjunction with, or in respect of any other damage or injury that may be so caused, nor do the Publishers accept responsibility in any way for the failure to obtain specified components.

Notice is also given that if equipment that is still under warranty is modified in any way or used or connected with home-built equipment then that warranty may be void.

© 1992 BERNARD BABANI (publishing) LTD

First Published – September 1992
Reprinted – July 1997

British Library Cataloguing in Publication Data
Brewster, R.
  The Art of Soldering
  I. Title
  671.5

  ISBN 0 85934 324 3

Cover Design by Gregor Arthur
Printed and bound in Great Britain by Cox & Wyman Ltd, Reading

Preface

To most people soldering is a subject which has to be dealt with occasionally and in most cases the odd repair job done is just acceptable but never understood.

This book will cover most aspects of soldering, from electronics to car radiators.

Richard Brewster

Contents

Chapter 1

CHOOSING YOUR SOLDERING IRON

What is a soldering iron? To some people it is a bit of plastic with a hot thing on the end which is used to stick bits of metal together, and apart from that it is a complete mystery.

The numbers and types of soldering iron on the market today make choosing the correct iron very difficult. It is essential that the correct iron is used for each job, but at this stage it must be emphasised that there is no such thing as a general purpose iron that will do all soldering jobs.

We will therefore deal with what you will need to know about the soldering iron when making your first purchase.

One major warning before we proceed. A modern soldering iron is a precision instrument and several manufacturers now make their elements with ceramic insulation. The purpose of this is to make the iron most suitable for use with modern electronic components and it does of course mean that the iron must be treated very much more carefully than in the past. You must never knock the solder off the end of the bit, drop the iron, use it to force a part out of its connection or apply excess pressure to the handle when soldering. All these actions will cause the ceramic insulation to break causing premature element failure. Please do not then blame the manufacturer as it is an operator fault not a manufacturing fault.

The factors you need to consider when selecting your soldering iron can be broken down as follows:

(i)   What type shall I choose?

(ii) If electrical, what voltage shall I choose?

(iii) What wattage do I need?

(iv) What size of iron do I need?

Let us deal with these in order.

Type
Portable Gas: This type of iron is becoming very popular because it is the first useful type of portable iron available. Providing you have a canister of gas available to refill the iron then it will be able to be used over a long period. This type of iron tends to be available only in the range up to 50 watts for standard soldering and is therefore only useful for the smaller job. However, it comes very much into its own for field work where power is not available. The other main advantage is its lack of a cable. Some of the more expensive units do have a flame head available as an extra. This will of course enable you to solder much larger items where the flame is not a problem.

Rechargeable: This was the first type of portable iron introduced many years ago. The biggest disadvantage with this type is its limited usage per charge. Most irons of this type will, theoretically, give you up to 100 joints per charge, which in most cases is per 24 hours. However, my experience is that this translates in practice to only 4 minutes continuous use in the 24 hour period between charges. This can be extended by having the iron continually on charge when not in use.

Electrical: This will be the most popular type chosen but even here the choice will be wide. Electrical soldering irons have been around for years and are therefore the type most of us are used to. They range from cheap imported irons (suitable only for general purpose soldering around the house or car) to very expensive solder stations suitable only for industry.

So what factors need to be considered when purchasing or selecting the type of iron needed for your particular application?

Voltage
The voltage you choose will be dependent on where or how you intend to use the iron.

2

220–240 Volt: This will be the most popular choice and is therefore the most common voltage of soldering irons available in the United Kingdom and Europe.

100–120 Volt: This voltage is mainly used in the Far East or the United States and Canada. However, it is now commonly used on building sites and other primary installations in the building and construction trades. Unless you have this voltage available then 100–120 volts should be avoided and under no circumstances should the iron be plugged directly into a 240-volt mains supply.

24 Volt: This is a specialist voltage and again unsuitable for domestic use. Some factories now work with 24 volts. One other use tends to be for irons that are plugged into solder stations. These are only suitable for that use and for no other.

12 Volt: This is the other popular voltage and can be used wherever a suitable 12-volt power supply is available. One word of warning though. Most people do not realise that when the voltage is decreased then the current INCREASES. Therefore even small items at 12 volts will use large amounts of current (amps). A simple rule of thumb is that for every 25 watts of device you require 2 amps of power at 12 volts. It will therefore be seen that a 1.5 amp model railway transformer is not suitable for a 25-watt soldering iron and will probably burn out in a very short time. It will also be seen that 12 volts is really impractical for soldering irons with a wattage greater than say 50 watts, due to the cost and size of the transformer system required as well as the cable size that would need to be fitted to prevent the cable catching fire.

What Wattage Do I Need?
If you have already been looking at soldering irons you have probably been baffled by all the different wattages that are on the market. You will probably have seen 12, 15, 18, 20, 25, 30, 40, 50 watt ratings and many more, even though many of them look to be the same size physically.

These variations are explained by the different designs of soldering iron and their various efficiencies. The wattage tells you only how much electricity the product will use and not its heat related performance, which is determined by the amount of heat that the element can transfer to the soldering bit before the bit cools off.

There are three main designs of iron currently available (see Figure 1.1).

(a) The Bit Sliding Over the Element: This type of iron is the most efficient, in that all the heat from the element must pass through the bit to get to the air. Therefore, with this type of construction a smaller wattage of iron can be used against the other two types.

(b) The Bit Sliding Inside the Element: This is the most inefficient construction, having a large surface area of the element exposed to the air as against the bit. This type of iron would only be about 40% as efficient as the type (a).

(c) The Bit Screwed Onto the Element Block: This style is more efficient than (b) but much less efficient than (a). Its biggest drawback is that if the bit seizes onto the element block then the element will either be seriously damaged or destroyed rendering the iron completely useless.

This therefore explains the various wattages on the market and in my experience a 25-watt version of style (b) is equivalent to an 18-watt version of style (a) or a 22-watt version of style (c).

What Size of Iron Do I Need?
As mentioned at the beginning of the book there is no such thing as a general purpose soldering iron. Most irons are available with interchangeable bits to give them a wider sphere of use but even here the applications would be limited within the range of the iron. For example, an 18-watt iron should be available with bit sizes from 1.5mm to 6mm, the 1.5mm size being suitable for micro electronic circuits and the 6mm for slightly thicker wires.

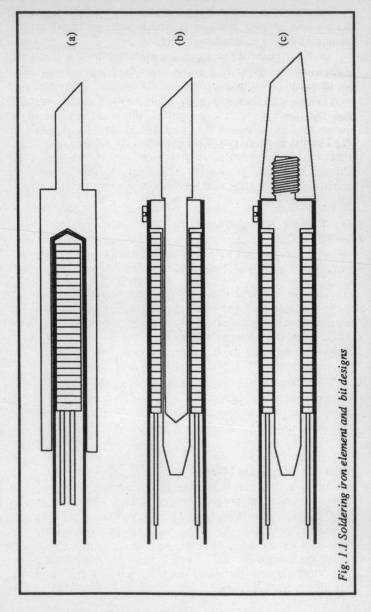

Fig. 1.1 Soldering iron element and bit designs

Throughout the book I will try to recommend the type and size of iron as well as solder types and voltages that I would recommend for a particular application.

One final point when buying a soldering iron is that you must decide whether it is going to be used regularly or only occasionally. This will determine the type of iron you will buy. Make sure that spares, especially bits, are easily available and that there is a simple guarantee. If you are not sure as to the availability of spares then you should consider purchasing them at the same time as you buy the original soldering iron.

Chapter 2

ACCESSORIES

There are many accessories available all of which are useful for particular applications. This chapter deals with the most popular ones that you may wish to purchase when you buy your soldering iron.

Stand

The soldering iron stand is one of the more important accessories available and is especially necessary for electrical soldering irons. It must be remembered that the soldering iron bit is probably at a temperature in excess of 400°C when at rest and apart from the obvious electrical problems of pulling the plug out when tripping over the lead or of melting through the cable, there is also the problem of ruining clothing or tattooing your body! Many a hobbyist has a burn mark on their stomach where they have accidentally leaned over the bench where the soldering iron has been hooked onto a nail at the edge of the bench. It is very easy to do and very painful.

There are two basic types of stand available on the market at present, the spring type and the metal fully enclosed type.

The spring type (Figure 2.1) is the most common but must be treated more carefully. In the cheaper versions it is possible for the weight of the soldering iron to bend the spring sufficiently to allow the soldering iron bit to touch the spring, so that the spring eventually becomes very hot and again can cause serious burns when touched. Make sure when buying that the spring stand is strong enough for the iron you have and that the bit cannot touch the spring. Make sure also that the stand has a very heavy base otherwise the whole lot could be as dangerous as the use without the stand. It is my experience that most spring stands would need to be screwed down to be fully safe but I am sure that this would not go down very well at home if you should screw it to the front room table!

The metal fully enclosed stand (Figure 2.2) is the better type. Not only does it tend to allow the bit to be fully enclosed and away from any metalwork, but because of its construction

7

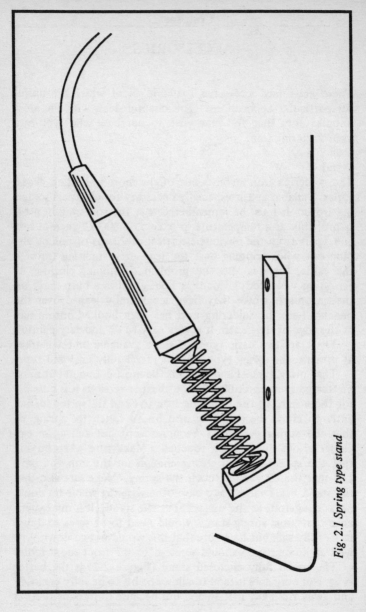

Fig. 2.1 Spring type stand

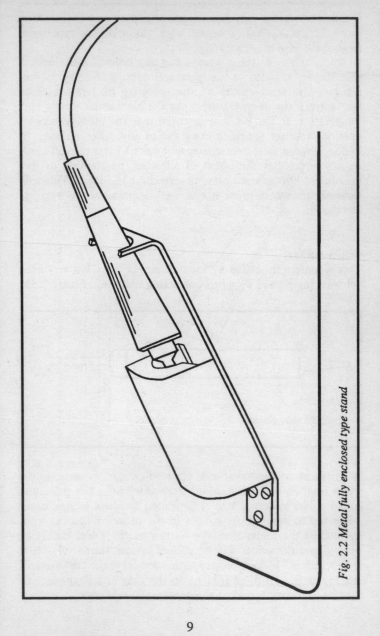

Fig. 2.2 Metal fully enclosed type stand

it tends to have a very low centre of gravity and is therefore more difficult to knock or pull over. Most of this type tend to hold the iron more securely.

One word of warning when using any type of stand with a soldering iron with a temperature control facility which registers the temperature of the soldering iron rather than just adjusts the temperature. As the electronics detect the temperature at the bit it is essential that the bit is **always** in open air and not touching the stand or any other surface. If it does then a false message is sent back to the control electronics which has the effect of allowing the element of the iron to get hotter and hotter to overcome the load. This will seriously reduce element life as well as prematurely burning out the bit.

Solder Sucker

This is sometimes called a "vacuum pump", and is a very useful tool for repairs or when correcting mistakes (Figure 2.3).

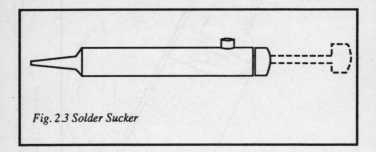

Fig. 2.3 Solder Sucker

It works in conjunction with your soldering iron and, as its name implies, sucks the solder from the joint. The principle of the solder sucker is that it is primed and held in one hand while the soldering iron is held in the other. When the iron has melted the solder then the button on the solder sucker is pressed and the solder will be sucked up into the barrel of the solder sucker. If done properly, this will leave the area around the repair free of most solder. In the case of a larger area it may be necessary to repeat the process several times.

If used carefully then it is possible to remove solder from all the pins of an integrated circuit (chip) to enable it to be removed without damaging the circuit board. This will be dealt with further in later chapters.

De-solder Braid

This is another repair product and is actually copper braid (Figure 2.4) which is laid on the area where solder needs to be removed. The main problems with this product are, firstly that you will need a large soldering iron bit to heat it up, and secondly if the solder is allowed to cool before the braid is removed then there is a serious danger of the printed circuit track being lifted from the board thus destroying the circuit board. Having said that, the de-solder braid is a very useful item for removing larger amounts of soldering providing the dangers outlined above are overcome.

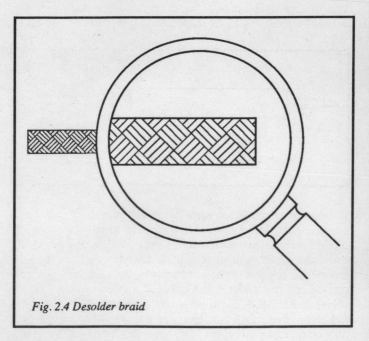

Fig. 2.4 Desolder braid

Chapter 3

FLUXES

The purpose of flux is to enable the solder to attach itself to the job in hand. This sounds easy but if the wrong flux is chosen then there is the serious possibility of the flux corroding the joint and thereby causing it to fail (come apart). It will therefore be seen that the type of flux chosen is very important. If you feel you need a strong flux then you are probably not cleaning the work sufficiently before soldering.

Inert Fluxes: This type of flux is the most common and is the type that should be used for most electronic and modelling work. Its main property is that it is only active when it is heated and then tends to burn off. One variant of this type, often called "rosin flux", tends to be very sticky.

Active Fluxes: This type of flux is useful for more difficult materials such as lead but should **never** be used on thin material such as copper or brass as it will corrode the material very quickly. Before using any type of flux it is a good idea to apply a small amount to an unimportant part of the work. If the area is brightened then this is an active flux and its use should be thought about very carefully and, if possible, avoided.

Most active fluxes are either very acidic or very alkaline. They do not burn off like the inert type but remain active for a very long time. It can therefore be seen that if this type is used on a printed circuit board or a precious model then it will not take the flux long to destroy the work. I have indeed seen a very nice model locomotive hit the buffers too hard and become a construction kit again. The flux under the joints had remained active and gradually etched away under the joints.

A good example of this is available in the house. Check the joints on your copper water pipes. You will almost certainly find several of them coated with a green material.

This is in fact copper sulphate caused by a reaction between the copper pipe and the flux. You will also note that however many times you try to wash it off it always comes back.

In the early days of electronics a flux called "Arax" was in constant use. Arax is still available but tends to be used for soldering stainless steel or other materials which are hard to solder. It was found, after continuous failures of the printed circuit board, that the copper track was etched away under the solder joint thus causing early failure of the board. This can still happen today if the wrong flux is used.

Advice on choosing a suitable solder and flux for a particular job will be given in later chapters.

One final word of warning regarding flux. There are many concoctions on the market purporting to be flux. Most of these are not marked as to their hazard level. I have come across many that are lethal and which, if used in an industrial environment, would need respiratory apparatus and protective clothing. If the bottle or can is not marked as to its contents then do not buy it. In extreme circumstances it could be your life that you are playing with.

I have come across one such bottle whose contents, if used in a confined space without ventilation and with a full temperature soldering iron, would almost certainly cause the user to be overcome by toxic fumes. Beware of innocent looking bottles or cans. If you are doubtful about the flux you already have, or are about to buy, then ask the retailer or better still contact the manufacturer and demand to know the contents.

Under the Consumer Protection Regulations, manufacturers and suppliers of this type of material are legally bound, firstly to clearly mark the hazard level of their product on the bottle or can and, secondly, if required, to supply technical data on the product. If you are using these fluxes to manufacture models or other parts for resale then of course the regulations of the Health and Safety at Work Act apply. In this case it is a requirement of the Act that you know what you are using. All reputable manufacturers will be more than happy to supply you with this Health and Safety information, the others will not, which will enable you to make up your own mind as to whose fluxes to use! Your health may be at risk.

Chapter 4

SOLDER

There are a whole array of solders to choose from, some cheap and others high tech. Your choice is wide because each variety comes in a range of thicknesses. The optimum thickness of the solder will depend on the size of iron you are using. Many people use a solder which is too thick for the size of iron they are using. I would recommend solder thicknesses as follows:

Soldering Iron Size	*Solder Thickness*
Up to 20 watts, bit sizes up to 4.5mm	22 swg
20 watts to 40 watts	18 swg
40 watts to 100 watts	16—18 swg
100 watts upwards, bit sizes from 9.5mm	16 swg

It will be seen that even for the large iron, the recommended solder thickness is only 16 swg. There is no point in using all the power of the soldering iron to melt the solder. There will then be insufficient power left to heat the areas to be jointed, which will only cause a dry joint.

You should avoid buying solder which is not marked with the type or the quantity. Some of the cheap tubes contain only small quantities of very poor solder aimed at the totally inexperienced D-I-Y user and totally unsuitable for proper soldering. Try to select a proprietory name such as "Multicore", "Frys", etc., and a type which clearly indicates what it is and what flux it contains, if any.

Pre-Fluxed Solders
Most solders you will buy are pre-fluxed, including most of the solders mentioned below with the exception of plumbers'

solder. It will be quite rare nowadays to find a quality solder that is not pre-fluxed and therefore care must be taken if you decide to add an extra flux, to ensure that the two fluxes do not react with each other. In pre-fluxed solders the flux is contained in cores which run throughout its whole length (Figure 4.1).

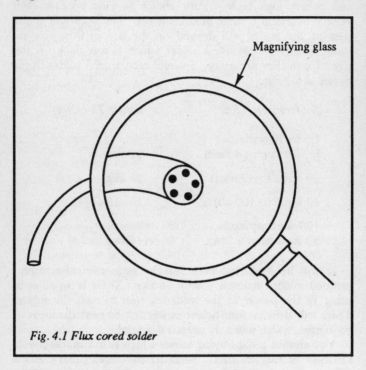

Fig. 4.1 Flux cored solder

The types generally available are as follows:

Savbit: This is the type I would recommend for most modelling and electronic work. It is available in most sizes and contains in-built inert flux. The advantage of this solder over the standard 60/40 variety is that it contains a small amount of copper which in my experience, considerably lengthens the life of the soldering iron bit. The theory is that the copper is absorbed by the chemical reaction and prevents the soldering iron bit from deteriorating instead. I would point out that Savbit is a trade mark of Multicore Solders Ltd, although a similar product is available from other manufacturers.

60/40 Tin/Lead: This has been the most widely used solder over the years. Most of us can find some of this in our possession. It is my opinion that this type has been superseded by the Savbit type, but it is still very suitable for most uses. However, it is recommended that it should be used only with iron-coated soldering iron bits. It was because of the etching effect of this type of solder that the iron-plated bit was introduced in the first place.

40/60 Tin/Lead: This has a lower melting point than the two previously mentioned types and often comes with a more active flux. I would not recommend its use for electronics, but it would be very suitable for stained glass work, etc.

Arax 95/5 Tin/Antimony: This solder has a very corrosive flux and is very suitable for stainless steel and other materials requiring a more aggressive flux content. You should not use it on electronics or models unless you are prepared to thoroughly scrub the work afterwards to remove the excess flux.

Alusol: This is a specialist solder intended, as its name implies, for soldering aluminium. It has been specially formulated for that use and again should not be used for other applications. Alusol is a registered trade mark of Multicore Solders Ltd.

Plumbers: The modern plumbers' solder must not contain lead if being used with water. This type of solder usually comes in much thicker sizes than most, and would usually be used with a blow torch. It would be mostly unsuitable for jobs where a soldering iron would be used.

Solder Paste: This material is really for an emergency repair, although some people do use it instead of ordinary solder.

Solder Tape: This really is for that emergency repair. It is designed to melt by using a match or cigarette lighter, and is unsuitable for use with a soldering iron.

Low-melt Solder: This is a specialist solder sold mainly for builders of white-metal kits in the model railway and wargame market. Some low-melt solders melt at a very low temperature which it is virtually impossible to get down to even with a very accurate temperature controlled soldering iron. This of course means that they will be very difficult to work with. If the white metal needs a solder with this low a melting temperature, then it also may be very difficult to work with. The best type of low-melt solder melts around 140°C.

Chapter 5

SAFETY

One aspect of soldering that must be dealt with at the outset is that of safety. A lot of accidents, especially in the home, are caused by soldering irons. Most, if not all, could be avoided if more care was exercised right from the beginning.

It must always be remembered that a soldering iron is very hot while it is on, but will not convey that message to you until you have touched it, at which time it is too late. **Always** put the soldering iron in a stand or other secure holder when you are not using it and **never** rest it loosely or hook it onto the bench or table. This is especially important with the larger irons which could give you a very serious burn or be pulled by their cable onto a carpet and cause a fire.

Safety and Children

Make sure that your children cannot accidentally pull the soldering iron off the bench or, worse still, pick it up by the hot end, especially when switched on. I have known this happen on several occasions and if this is done with a larger soldering iron it will cause severe burns. It is advisable to keep children under 8 years of age away from your soldering equipment. If you are going to teach your children to solder please explain to them the dangers involved. I have previously mentioned the dangers regarding fluxes. If children are around, make sure that all of these bottles or tins are securely locked away because they will be very attractive to children. Do not let them handle the solder because it contains lead. If they then put it into their mouths they could become quite ill. Make sure that both you and your family thoroughly wash your hands after you or they have been handling solder before eating or handling food.

With gas irons **never** turn the gas valve unless you are ready to ignite the iron as this may cause an explosion when it is eventually lit. Butane gas is very difficult to detect but very easy to light.

With mains electrical irons always check the cable for burns. You could have burnt through the insulation and exposed a live wire which could kill if touched. Always replace damaged cables with a proper cable. Never fit a smaller cable than that originally fitted by the manufacturer. His first aim was safety. Always make sure that the plug is fitted properly and that, in the U.K. especially, you fit a correctly rated fuse to the plug.

Fusing

Whilst most suppliers recommend a 3 amp fuse it is my opinion that this is too large and a fuse of 1 amp is more appropriate. These are not easily obtainable in the 1 inch size which fits the standard U.K. 13 amp BS.1363 plug, and you may have to settle for the 2 amp rating.

On a 240V mains supply, the current consumption for various wattage irons is as follows:

Wattage	Current (Amps)
18	0.075
25	0.105
50	0.210
100	0.420
250	1.040

As will be seen, a 1 amp fuse is sufficient right up to 200 watts. It is my opinion that a 3 amp fuse is no protection at all until you get to 250 watts, and there are not very many soldering irons of that wattage around. Fitting a 13 amp fuse in the plug of your 18 watt iron would be the equivalent to fitting a 2167 amp fuse to your 3 kW electric fire. I am sure you would not do that, so why risk your life by doing it to your soldering iron. People have said to me "but the iron works with the 13 amp fuse in the plug". What can you say? The fuse is there to protect both the user, and possibly their property, only when the product goes wrong.

One final point regarding safety. All items used with soldering are dangerous in one way or another. Please stop and think before commencing with soldering so that you can have a successful and accident-free time with your hobby. The watchword is THINK!

Chapter 6

STARTING TO SOLDER

Regardless of the items you are going to solder, there are several steps which must be observed to enable you to get the best results.

The watchword of soldering is cleanliness. The more time you spend paying attention to the cleanliness of the joint then the more likely you are to get a good joint. The most common reason for a failed (dry) joint is that the parts to be soldered have not been cleaned properly. The other main reason why joints fail is because the size of soldering iron or solder chosen is wrong for the work to be done. If the iron is too small then the soldered joint will not be heated sufficiently for good adhesion to take place. The same effect will apply if the solder is too thick and therefore draining too much heat out of the soldering iron.

At this point I must explain the difference between heat and temperature. This is usually the most misunderstood area of soldering.

Temperature: Most soldering irons of good design will run at about the same temperature, usually between 350°C and 500°C. Soldering irons that run at temperatures greater than 500°C should be avoided or controlled as the bit will quickly oxidise and cause poor soldering and excessive bit wear.

Heat: This is a much better indicator of the power of the soldering iron. Unfortunately there is not an accepted unit to indicate the heat of the soldering iron. Needless to say the theory is that the bigger the bit then the greater the heat content. The only limitation to this is the capability of the soldering iron element to replace the heat that the work has taken out. One mistake that is regularly made when choosing the size of soldering iron and its bit is to look at the size of the bit without taking into consideration the area of material around the joint.

The example which crops up more than any is the repair of the pin-hole in the car radiator. Many people cannot understand why, when the hole is only very small, their small soldering iron with say a 1.5mm or 3mm bit will not make the repair. The simple answer is that the area of metal around the repair must be heated up to at least the melting point of the solder used. My experience is that a soldering iron of at least 500 watts would be needed but that a blow torch would be better.

Preparing to Solder

A common mistake when first starting work with a new soldering iron or new soldering bit is the failure to properly tin the surface of the bit as it heats up. Many people complain that they cannot get their new iron to melt the solder even though the iron appears to be hot enough. The answer is very simple. Unless the bit is tinned successfully when new and at regular intervals an oxidising surface will cover the bit. This will reject the solder and give the impression that the soldering iron is not hot enough to melt the solder. Sometimes you can turn the soldering iron off and then wipe the surface with a damp sponge and try again. However, this seldom works and the soldering iron bit can only be recovered by using an abrasive on the surface and then starting again.

It must be remembered that the life of the soldering iron bit is only as good as its coating. If you file or sand through that coating to enable you to re-tin the bit then it will only last as long as one of the standard copper variety. It is no use complaining to the manufacturer that his expensive long-life bit has lasted only a short time because the fault is entirely yours.

Tinning the Bit

A considerable amount of patience is required here as the bit must be tinned exactly at the moment that the bit temperature reaches the melting point of your solder (Figure 6.1(a)). The method adopted is very simple as follows:

(i)   Turn your soldering iron on to heat up.
(ii) If you are using flux-free solder then apply flux to the

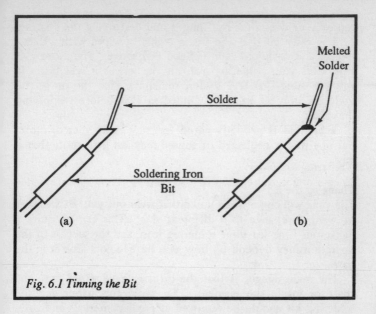

Solder

Melted Solder

Soldering Iron Bit

(a)   (b)

Fig. 6.1 Tinning the Bit

end of the soldering iron bit. If the solder you are using contains flux then this step is not necessary.

(iii)   Hold the solder against the flat face of the bit and wait and be patient.

(iv)   After a short time the solder should be seen to start melting. As soon as this happens move the solder around the flat face of the bit, ensuring that it is well covered (Figure 6.1(b)).

(v)   Wipe the solder off with a damp sponge. You should see that the flat surface of the bit is now evenly coated with a thin layer of solder.

(vi)   If you have successfully achieved (v) then reapply solder to the bit and you are ready to start soldering.

Having achieved successful tinning then it is essential to keep this appearance at the end of the bit at all times.

Never allow flux to build up and then leave the soldering iron switched on for long periods when not in use. This will cause an unsolderable build-up on the end of the bit which can only be overcome by filing it and destroying the coating.

It is essential that the bit is regularly wiped with a damp sponge and re-tinned as in (v) and (vi) above. The more you look after your soldering iron bit the longer it will last. If you are using flux-free solder, remember that the tip of the soldering iron bit must be dipped in flux before reapplying the solder.

A bit that is properly cared for may last a year or more, but one that is neglected or abused may last little more than a day.

Changing the Bit

The time will come when you either wear out your existing bit or want to change to a different size. This can be quite a dangerous time for your soldering iron, and the success of the operation may depend on how you have looked after it in the past.

The main danger is that the bit may have seized onto the shaft or inside the element. To avoid this happening the soldering bit should be removed at regular intervals and carefully refitted. **Never** clamp the iron or the bit in any way to remove the bit and **always** pull the bit directly off. If you try to twist or bend the bit to get it off, there is a very high chance of destroying the element of the soldering iron.

With the type of soldering iron where the bit slides inside the element, a seized bit is often fatal. The only recourse you have is to file the bit every time it oxidises until it is too short to work with, at which time the soldering iron will have to be discarded. It is therefore very important that the bit on this type of soldering iron is removed regularly to prevent seizure.

With the type where the bit screws onto the element, it is again essential that the bit be removed regularly and refitted with a coating of anti-seize grease on the thread. Once again seizure of the bit will mean the premature disposal of the soldering iron.

Finally, with the type where the bit slides over the element, seizure is not usually a problem as the shaft is usually made of stainless steel and therefore the bit can be carefully removed. Before replacing the bit on this type of iron, you may find it helps to repolish the stainless steel shaft using very fine wet-and-dry abrasive paper in its wet state. This will remove any scale that may have built up and make the shaft of the soldering iron smooth and shiny again. Before refitting the bit, ensure that it fits snugly over the shaft, and that the clip holds the bit tightly onto the shaft. If the clip is loose then replace it unless by reshaping it you can get it tight again. Think what could happen if the bit falls off onto your lap when it is hot!

Chapter 7

THE DRY JOINT

The term 'dry joint', which is used frequently throughout this book, warrants further explanation at this point.

The 'dry joint' is the most likely fault in soldering, and is the biggest single cause of failure, especially in electronics. The main causes of the dry joint are too small a soldering iron or bit and dirty work.

What is a Dry Joint?

Simply explained, a dry joint is what occurs when the soldered joint appears to be made but where, due to insufficient heat or dirty work, the solder has in fact not taken properly. The problem with a dry joint is that it appears to work, indeed it could work properly for years, but eventually fails. A dry joint is very difficult to see, as the failure point is between the solder and the work. In technical terms a dry joint is caused by oxidisation between the solder and the materials being jointed. In the case of electrical joints, this causes the electricity to jump across the joint rather than flow. In time, this will cause micro sparking across the joint which will eventually fail.

It is simple to demonstrate the mechanical side of a dry joint. Find a piece of metal which is too large for your soldering iron to solder, I would suggest a piece of steel about 1/16 of an inch thick. Clean it thoroughly by removing all the grease and dirt. Now try to solder a wire to it by applying the soldering iron to the wire and plate and adding solder. After a while the solder will appear to flow and also the wire will appear to stick to the plate. You should then be able to lift the plate with the wire.

Now test the joint by holding the plate and pulling the wire over the joint, as shown in Figure 7.1. If the experiment has worked the wire will peel away from the plate without breaking. This will be a true dry joint. Close inspection will show the joint to be dull matt grey in colour and if viewed through a magnifying glass will show small bubbles all over the joint

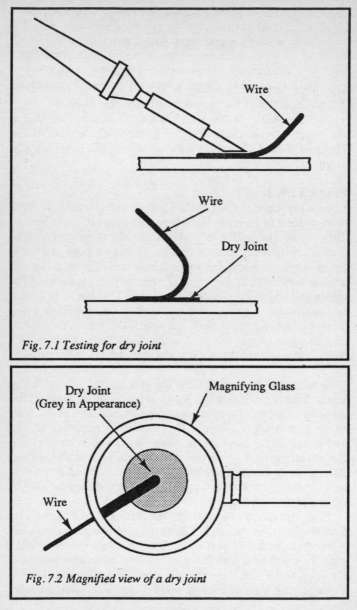

Wire

Wire

Dry Joint

Fig. 7.1 Testing for dry joint

Dry Joint
(Grey in Appearance)

Magnifying Glass

Wire

Fig. 7.2 Magnified view of a dry joint

(Figure 7.2). These bubbles would eventually cause complete failure of the joint both electrically and mechanically. As you can see it is almost impossible to detect a dry joint with the naked eye. It is therefore very important that particular attention is paid to the recommendations given as to soldering iron size and solder types for each type of work, in order to avoid this problem.

Chapter 8

SOLDERING AND ELECTRONICS

The most common application for soldering is in the construction and repair of electronic equipment.

Equipment Recommendations

Soldering Irons

All types of gas irons and rechargeable irons are suitable for work on electronic equipment. Electric soldering irons for electronic work should have a power of less than 25 watts. Most circuit boards would tend to be assembled and repaired with a 15- or 18-watt soldering iron.

With modern electronics it is essential that the iron has a very low leakage factor (check this with the retailer when buying). This is a measure of the quality and efficiency of the element's insulation to earth. There is a minimum legal requirement for this factor under the Consumer Protection Regulations, but if the soldering iron you have purchased only just complies with this level then it is my recommendation that this is inadequate for use with electronics. You should use a soldering iron with a leakage factor better than $1\mu A$ tested at not less than 1500 volts **hot**. A cold test would not give a good enough result. If the manufacturer of your soldering iron does not quote these figures in his leaflet or instructions then please check first. At the same time it is advisable for the bit to be earthed.

With an unearthed tip it may be necessary to use an earthed wrist and work strap to avoid problems when soldering sensitive electronic components. Not all components are that sensitive, and apart from CMOS devices it is unlikely that the hobbyist will come up against components that are that sensitive.

Whilst it is unlikely that the hobbyist will find them necessary or financially desirable, the solder station is available and would be used for most electronic assembly in the industrial environment. It is my opinion that these are unnecessary for the hobby user. It is also important that the iron be used at its full temperature (400°C), so a temperature control facility is not necessary. The hotter the iron (within reason), the quicker the joint will be made and the shorter the distance the heat will travel into the component.

As to bit size, a 3mm bit is very suitable for most soldering activities on printed circuit boards although for very fine integrated circuits you may be happier with a 1 to 1.5mm bit. For larger areas of copper you will probably need a 4.5 or 6mm bit for satisfactory soldering.

Solder Types
The selection of solder for electronics is very important. It is essential that only solder containing inert flux is used. No other type of pre-fluxed solder is acceptable, especially where only thin tracks exist on the circuit board. Suitable solders are 60/40 or "Savbit".

I would recommend that 22 swg solder is thick enough for all electronic work. The use of a thicker gauge will only mean that more solder than necessary will be used, and there is a great chance that it will flow over circuit tracks that should not be joined together.

Flux
As mentioned already, only an inert flux should be used. If the work has been cleaned properly then it should not be necessary to use a flux in addition to pre-fluxed solder. Remember, if you are unsure of the type of flux you are using then test it on a waste piece of circuit board first.

Solder Sucker
A solder sucker will be found to be very useful for repair work.

Small Pliers
These also will be found to be very useful, both for positioning components and for removing them from the board when making repairs. They will also help you to avoid the temptation to prise the component from the board with the soldering iron.

Small Side-Cutters
These will be essential for cutting off the excess component wires to prevent them touching other tracks.

Damp Sponge
This is essential for the regular wiping of the soldering iron bit to keep it clean.

Learning to Solder
Most people's first attempt at soldering with electronics will involve the use of stripboard. This is a very useful material and prevents the use of many wires to connect the components to each other. It comes in several different sizes and is easy to cut into the size you require. I would suggest however that you do not cut it until you have successfully completed your circuit. There is nothing more frustrating than finding you have done most of the circuit but have insufficient room for the last few components. Like printed circuit boards, stripboard must be soldered correctly and carefully to prevent the bridging of two or more strips.

Before actually soldering components into the board, it is a good idea to practise soldering wires to the end of the strips without bridging the tracks, in the following manner.

1. Tin the Wires to be Soldered (Figure 8.1) The purpose of pre-tinning the wires is to enable the soldering iron to make the final joint without the need to apply additional solder. You will need to use a soldering iron bit of at least 3mm for this process. A 1mm or 1.5mm bit is too small and will only cause a dry joint. Proceed as follows:

   (i)   Remove the outer insulation from the wire; about 4mm will be enough.

   (ii) Make sure that the soldering iron tip is properly tinned.

  (iii) Apply the soldering iron bit to the wire.

  (iv) Apply the solder to the wire (not to the soldering iron bit). This will enable you to see when the wire is hot enough to melt the solder properly. The solder will then be seen to flow smoothly over the wire. When sufficient solder has melted onto the

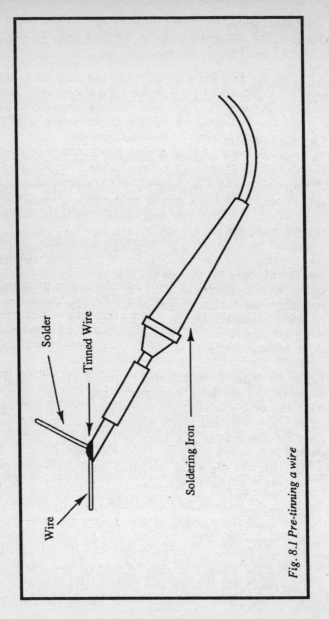

Solder

Tinned Wire

Soldering Iron

Wire

Fig. 8.1 Pre-tinning a wire

wire (the wire should be fully covered by solder) remove the solder and the soldering iron and allow the wire to cool.

2. Tinning the Board (Figure 8.2) Like the wire, the board will be easier to solder to if it has been pre-tinned. This unfortunately cannot be done when a component has to be inserted into the holes of the board, as pre-tinning will fill the holes and prevent insertion of the component.

Tinning the board, or even soldering to it, has to be done very carefully to prevent the solder flowing from one track to another. It will be a good idea to practice applying solder to the strips before going to the next stage. The size of soldering iron bit should not exceed the width of the copper on the track. Proceed as follows:

(i) Make sure that the soldering iron bit is fully tinned as previously described. For this operation ensure that the bit is not heavily loaded with excess solder.

(ii) Apply the soldering iron bit to the copper strip, and after a few seconds apply the solder to the strip. Do not allow the solder to flow other than towards the bit. Slant the bit away from the melting solder and finish applying the solder to the end of the strip and remove the soldering iron completely.

If you have been successful then the solder should be slightly humped, with a high point along the centre of the strip, and be shiny in appearance (Figure 8.3). If the solder is grey in colour then it may not have properly attached itself to the copper strip. If you have a magnifying glass available, look carefully at the strip and make sure that not even a whisker of solder has attached itself to one or other strip at either side (Figure 8.4). If it is clear then you have success-fully tinned the strip.

Now you can become more adventurous, and try to do the same to one of the adjacent strips. Follow the same pro-cedure, taking great care to ensure that you do not melt the solder on the strip previously completed. If you do there is every chance that you will solder the two tracks together. As mentioned before, the soldering iron bit used must not be wider than the board's track, otherwise it would then melt the

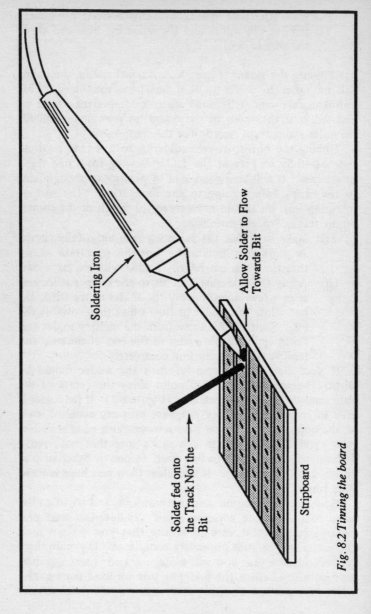

Soldering Iron

Allow Solder to Flow Towards Bit

Solder fed onto the Track Not the Bit

Stripboard

Fig. 8.2 Tinning the board

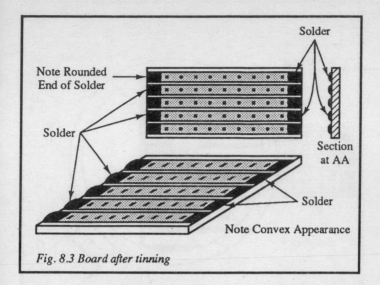

Fig. 8.3 Board after tinning

solder over more than one track with the inevitable result of soldering those two tracks together.

When you have satisfactorily tinned several tracks, and inspected them, you can solder the wires to them that you prepared earlier. If all preparation work has been satisfactorily completed then no additional solder will be required for this stage. Proceed as follows:

(i)   Check that the soldering iron bit is properly clean and tinned as before. If not then re-tin.

(ii) Hold the tinned part of the wire exactly parallel with the strip (Figure 8.5). It is very important that the wire is not at even the slightest angle as there is then the possibility of overlapping to the next track.

(iii) Place the soldering iron bit on to the wire (not the track) and watch the solder melt around the wire and then the track (Figure 8.6).

(iv) When the solder on the track has melted remove the soldering iron.

(v)   This stage is the most important of all. It is vital that the wire is held completely still while the solder cools. Even if the wire is only moved slightly, it will

39

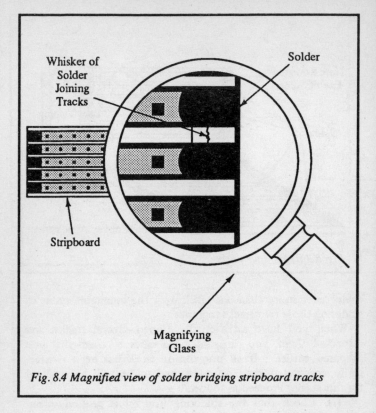

Whisker of Solder Joining Tracks

Solder

Stripboard

Magnifying Glass

Fig. 8.4 Magnified view of solder bridging stripboard tracks

cause a failed joint. Be patient and even if you think the solder has cooled, wait a bit longer. Moving the wire before the solder has cooled properly is the cause of many a dry joint.

Once again it will help you if you can inspect the joint through a magnifying glass to ensure that neither the solder nor the wire has strayed over to an adjoining track (Figure 8.7). Now try to attach more wires again being very careful not to touch adjoining tracks.

If you now cut a small section off the main board, say about 2 inches along the strips, it will then be possible to solder wires to the other ends of the strips. This will enable

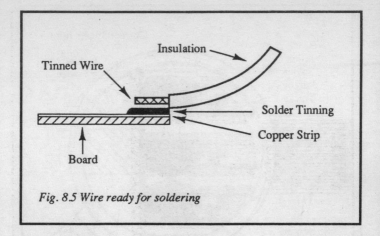

Fig. 8.5 Wire ready for soldering

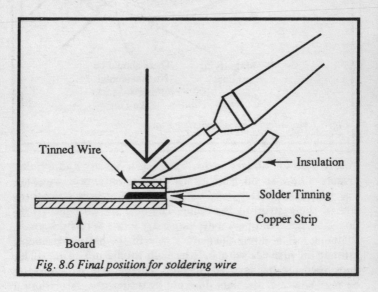

Fig. 8.6 Final position for soldering wire

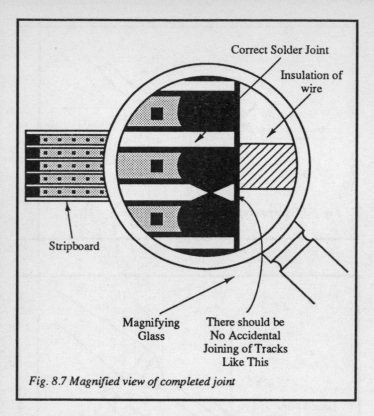

Correct Solder Joint

Insulation of wire

Stripboard

Magnifying Glass

There should be No Accidental Joining of Tracks Like This

Fig. 8.7 Magnified view of completed joint

you to test for bridged strips by using a battery and a bulb (Figure 8.8). To do this, attach the two outermost wires at one end to the battery and connect the wires from the other end of those strips to the bulb. The bulb should light. If it does not light then you may have a dry joint, so recheck your soldering. If it does, then move one of the battery connections to an adjacent wire and the bulb should not light. If it does, then the tracks are connected together and will need to be resoldered. If the light does not light then congratulations, those two tracks have been successfully soldered. Before finally celebrating, check all the other tracks in the same way.

As can be seen, it is very easy to make silly mistakes by letting the solder flow from one track to the other as you are

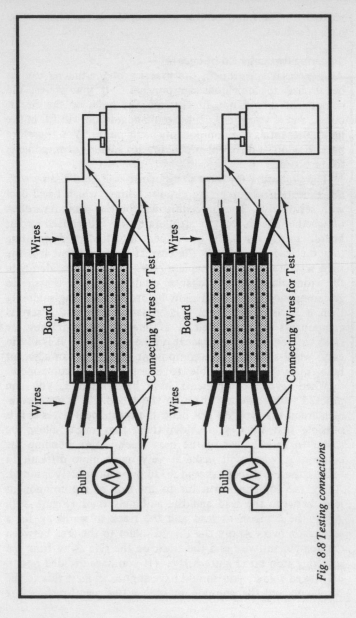

Fig. 8.8 Testing connections

soldering. The more careful you are, the better chance you have of success.

Soldering Particular Components

As previously mentioned, the practice of pre-tinning cannot be applied to individual components. If you pre-tin the component it will not fit through the holes on the circuit board, and if you pre-tin the circuit board you will fill in the holes, preventing the components being put in. You therefore have to adopt a different procedure for soldering components to the board.

The procedure for most components will be the same with the exception of integrated circuits (chips), which I will deal with separately. The procedure will be the same, regardless of whether the board is a stripboard or a full printed circuit board. Firstly insert the component into the board, ensuring that the leads go through the correct holes and that it is the right way around. I shall explain how to overcome soldering in the wrong place in a later chapter on desoldering. It is easier to get component placement right before commencing soldering than it is to correct it at a later date. It is best if several components are assembled at a time, especially if they are close to each other or adjacent on the same track. It is all too easy, when soldering one component lead, to fill an adjacent hole, making it impossible to insert a second component.

When several components have been inserted, you can proceed with soldering them to the board. It is my recommendation that you do **not** bend the component wires as it is possible that when you solder them they might allow the solder to spread over to the next track. Also, bending the component wires will make it very much more difficult to remove the component should it fail or be incorrectly inserted. Apply the soldering iron bit to the side of the component lead, between the lead and the adjoining track (Figure 8.9). Allow the component lead and the track to warm up for a second or two. Apply the fluxed solder to the area between the component wire and the track on the side away from the soldering iron bit (Figure 8.10). (If you have decided not to use fluxed solder, you should have applied an inert flux to the stripboard and the component with a fine paintbrush before

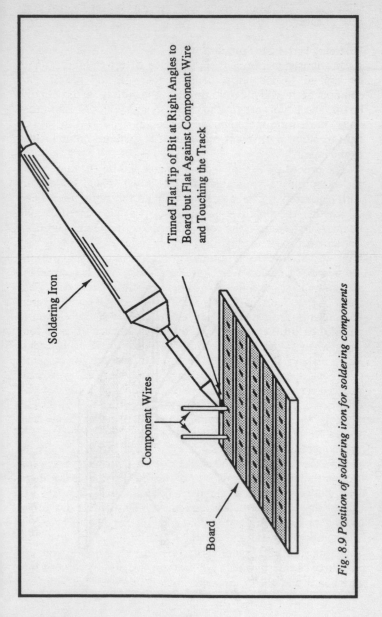

Soldering Iron

Tinned Flat Tip of Bit at Right Angles to Board but Flat Against Component Wire and Touching the Track

Component Wires

Board

Fig. 8.9 Position of soldering iron for soldering components

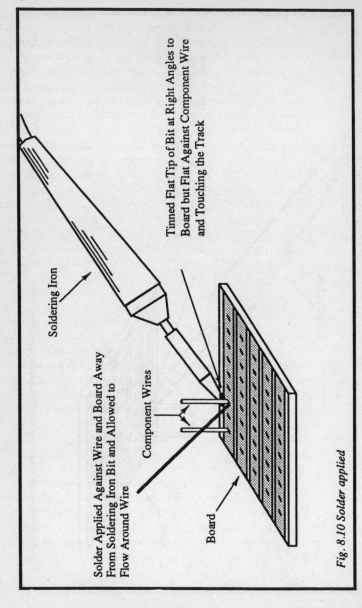

Soldering Iron

Solder Applied Against Wire and Board Away From Soldering Iron Bit and Allowed to Flow Around Wire

Component Wires

Tinned Flat Tip of Bit at Right Angles to Board but Flat Against Component Wire and Touching the Track

Board

Fig. 8.10 Solder applied

46

starting to solder – it sounds messy and it is.)

Watch the solder melt and flow around the component leg and along the track, ensuring that the solder melts on both the track and the component lead. When a reasonable amount of solder (too much will only cause problems so apply it with care) is smoothly around the component lead and on the track, remove the soldering iron and allow the joint to cool. This process should be very much shorter than the time it takes to explain. If you have successfully completed the joint, it should be shiny and form an oval mountain shape along the track with its peak on the component lead (Figure 8.11). On a full printed circuit board that has been properly prepared for components, this "mountain" might be circular instead of oval. Finally trim the wires as close to the solder joint as possible with a small flat-backed pair of side cutters. It does not matter if a small amount of the peak of the solder is cut off with the wire. One word of warning. If you connect the power to your circuit before you have properly cut off all the excess wires and before you have carefully checked for bridged or dry joints, then it is more than possible that you will damage components.

The worst case I have seen was a gentleman who knew nothing about electronics or soldering but decided to buy a 10-channel radio control transmitter and receiver kit by mail order. After many hours and many soldering mistakes which were eventually corrected (unfortunately for him not all), he decided to apply the power. One mistake he had not discovered was that the power leads were on the wrong way, so that when he applied the power all he got was smoke. He came to me to see what could be done, but I am afraid that my answer was to put it in the bin. He had no chance of finding the damage, which was probably extensive, and the cost would have been considerable had he employed an expert to repair it for him. The moral of the story is that you cannot check your joints and components enough times before applying the power. With many integrated circuits, electrolytic capacitors, transistors, etc., the wrong polarity can be fatal to the component, so take great care.

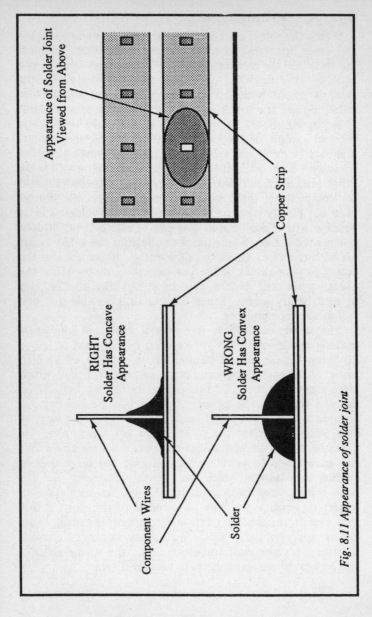

Fig. 8.11 Appearance of solder joint

Soldering Integrated Circuits

The simple answer to soldering integrated circuits (ICs) is don't unless it is unavoidable. Instead solder in an IC socket so that the IC itself can be plugged in later. This will save you a considerable number of problems at a later date should the IC need replacing. The procedure for soldering the socket is exactly the same as with the components, but obviously with so many leads in such a small space great care will have to be exercised to prevent bridging joints that should not be connected together. Some people prefer to use a smaller bit for ICs than other components, but remember that it is the size of the copper surrounding the joint rather than the size of the component that dictates the size of soldering iron bit to be used. Don't sacrifice the chance of a good joint for a smaller bit. Instead exercise more care to prevent the bridged joint.

Industrial Methods

Before leaving soldering and electronics, mention must be made of two modern methods of soldering which are used mainly in industry.

Flow Soldering: This is a production-line soldering system where all the components are inserted into the board, after which a conveyer system suspends the whole board over the solder bath; usually the heated solder is flowing across the bath. If the unit is correctly set then all joints will be properly soldered without the need for a soldering iron. The board is then passed over a cutting machine which trims the component wires to the correct length.

Unfortunately, even though extensive tests are applied after the boards have been soldered this system is prone to dry joints. Because of the widespread use of this system, the majority of faults in manufactured equipment are either dry joints or have been caused by dry joints. Hence the first thing to be done when repairing a failed circuit board is to go over the area of the fault with a soldering iron to remake the joints. It is surprising how many faults can be corrected in this way.

Soldering and Surface Mount Technology: Surface-mount technology is the latest system of printed circuit assembly used by industry. As the name suggests, the components are soldered onto the same side of the board as the printed track rather than the opposite side. This means that there are no wires on the components, but obviously this is not a practical system for the hobby user. In most cases very expensive and special tools and equipment have to be used.

Solder Pots

The solder pot is a very useful piece of equipment, especially if you have to tin many components or wires. The method of use is very simple and quick. The component or wire is dipped into a small pot of inert flux, after which it is dipped into the heated solder pot. After a short time the component or wire can be removed from the solder pot fully tinned.

Chapter 9

REPAIRS AND SOLDER REMOVAL

There are several ways of carrying out solder removal, most of which have been touched on earlier. Here we will discuss those ways in more detail.

The first and most unacceptable way is to try to remove the component by using the soldering iron to melt the solder from the circuit board and lever the component out before the solder hardens again. This would obviously work if there was only one wire involved, although when the component was out there is a great possibility that the hole vacated by the component would become blocked by the solder as it cools. This will prevent you putting in the new component without melting the solder yet again. This method can be very messy and cause solder to flow where you do not want it. There is even the possibility of overheating the circuit board track, causing it to lift from the main part of the board thus rendering the board useless. This method is obviously suitable for removing wires which are soldered to a surface, rather than being fitted through holes, and also for parting wires that are directly connected to each other or to switches, etc., but as previously shown it is totally unsuitable for circuit boards.

De-solder Braid
The next method is with de-solder braid. This method is acceptable and quicker for removing larger areas of solder but for continuous work it can be very expensive. One disadvantage, as has been mentioned in a previous chapter, is that you must use a larger bit than would usually be used for the circuit board. This is because there is a large volume of copper to be heated before the solder below will melt. The procedure is as follows (Figure 9.1):

(i) Lay the braid over the area where the solder is to be removed. You should only attempt a short distance at a time, say a quarter of an inch.
(ii) Apply the soldering iron bit over the braid where the solder is to be removed.

51

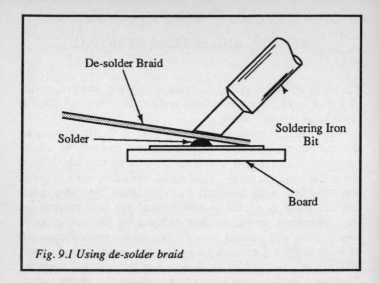

Fig. 9.1 Using de-solder braid

(iii) Watch the solder under the braid until it melts.

(iv) When it has satisfactorily melted, quickly remove the braid and the soldering iron together. It is extremely important that the braid is not allowed to cool at this stage, otherwise you will pull up the circuit board track with the braid and, as before, destroy the board.

(v) Repeat the procedure with any other solder you wish to remove, remembering that you can only use a piece of the braid once because when the braid is full of solder it cannot absorb any more. It is therefore wise to cut the used piece off the spool after each operation. Also remember that because it is copper braid the heat will travel rapidly along it, and can give you a nasty burn.

The Solder Sucker

The most commonly used way of de-soldering for the hobbyist is by using a solder sucker sometimes called a vacuum pump. This is a simple device very similar to a small bicycle pump except that it sucks rather than blows. The principle is that the vacuum sucks molten solder from the work and up into its barrel. If used properly and patiently then it is possible to remove almost all the solder from the work. In the case of a circuit board, it will allow even multi-pin devices to be removed without difficulty or the further use of a soldering iron. The solder sucker has to be used with a soldering iron to melt the solder before it is sucked up.

The method of use is simple and as follows:

(i) Make sure that the soldering iron is hot and the bit properly tinned.

(ii) Prime the solder sucker by pushing the pluger down until it latches.

(iii) Hold the solder sucker in one hand, the soldering iron in the other. Before you start, it is worth experimenting to see which hand you are happiest with for each device.

(iv) Hold the solder sucker on one side of the solder to be removed and the soldering iron at the other. Normally they should be at about 90° to each other and 45° to the board (Figure 9.2).

(v) Melt the solder with the soldering iron.

(vi) As the solder melts, quickly remove the soldering iron, bring the solder sucker upright and press the button on the solder sucker. If you have been quick enough then the solder will have been removed into the barrel of the solder sucker (Figure 9.3). If not, then it will have re-hardened on the work.

(vii) If you have successfully removed some or all of the unwanted solder, repeat the process on the rest of the job to be done. If not, repeat the process again on the area being worked.

It will be seen that practice will be needed to get the best results from the procedure, especially in judging when to remove the soldering iron and when to apply the solder sucker. Like most skilled operations you will eventually adopt your own method of successfully removing the solder.

One word of warning. When dealing with printed circuit board or stripboard do not keep the soldering iron in contact with the solder or the board longer than is necessary. Otherwise, as previously mentioned, you will lift the copper track away from the board causing virtually irreparable damage.

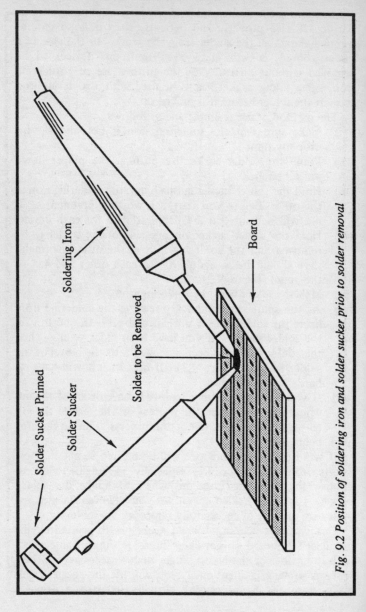

Fig. 9.2 Position of soldering iron and solder sucker prior to solder removal

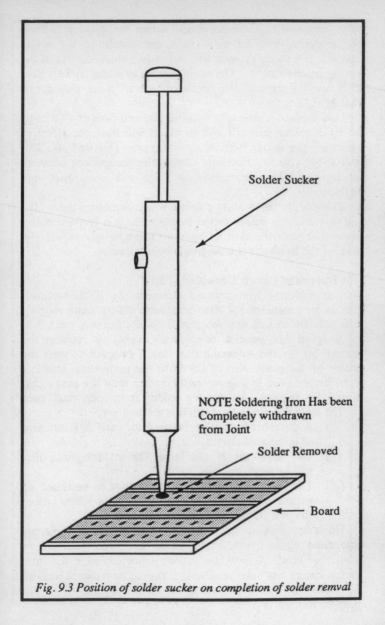

Solder Sucker

NOTE Soldering Iron Has been
Completely withdrawn
from Joint

Solder Removed

Board

Fig. 9.3 Position of solder sucker on completion of solder remval

Also, especially on cheaper model solder suckers, try to keep the soldering iron bit away from the nozzle of the solder sucker. If you don't, you will seriously reduce the life of the nozzle by melting it. The more expensive solder suckers have high melting temperature nozzles which are more resistant to that heat.

One useful technique is to allow the component wire to go into the solder sucker's nozzle which will have the effect of removing the solder from all round the wire (Figure 9.4). This will allow you to effectively unplug the component when all its legs are free, thus allowing quick and easy repair and replacement.

There is on the market a device which combines the soldering iron and the solder sucker in one tool. It is very expensive compared with the cost of the two items bought separately, and for the hobbyist it would be a luxury item.

The Integrated Circuit De-soldering Bit

Several soldering iron manufacturers supply IC de-soldering bits as an accessory for their products. As its name suggests it is only for unsoldering integrated circuits and is not suitable, or designed for, general de-soldering work. It replaces the normal bit on the soldering iron and is designed to melt the solder of the many pins of the IC at the same time, enabling it to be removed in one operation rather than the many that would be required in clearing solder from individual pins.

The main disadvantages with this method are:

(i) A different bit has to be used for each different size of integrated circuit.

(ii) The larger the IC the larger the soldering iron that will be required.

(iii) The board will almost certainly have to be tidied up with a soldering iron to remove excess solder before the new IC can be fitted.

However, if you are constantly repairing or replacing integrated circuits, this could be an invaluable addition to your tool box. As previously recommended, once the integrated circuit has been removed, it should be replaced with an IC socket so that if it fails in future it only has to be unplugged to remove it.

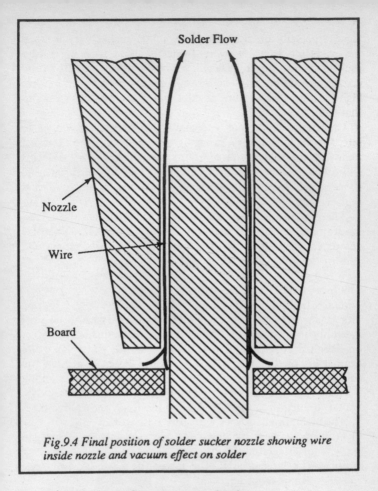

Fig.9.4 Final position of solder sucker nozzle showing wire inside nozzle and vacuum effect on solder

De-soldering and Surface Mount Technology

There are several types of complete de-soldering stations operating either by compressed air or by vacuum. Because of their cost, they are really only suitable for industrial use, and impractical for the hobby user.

A similar situation exists with de-soldering equipment intended for use with surface-mount technology. The equipment is very expensive and therefore outside the pocket of the average hobbyist.

Chapter 10

SOLDERING AND MODEL RAILWAYS

Model railways are probably the second most popular use for soldering. In this chapter I will cover soldering of all gauges from N to O and all aspects from trackwork to white metal.

Equipment Recommendations

Soldering Irons
All types of gas irons would be suitable for most applications especially for N and OO gauge although I would be doubtful as to their use in O gauge, unless the flame head is used, other than for electrical wiring. They would not be suitable for wiring to O-gauge track.

Rechargeable irons would only be suitable for soldering electronics and other small work around the layout. They are unlikely to be suitable for soldering to track in any gauge. As they would therefore have only a very limited use, they would not be very suitable for this application.

With electric types, obviously different sizes will be required for different gauges.

Voltage
Most people will use 240 volt soldering irons throughout their layout, although 12 volts is also a possibility. A word of warning when selecting a 12 volt soldering iron for this use. As I have mentioned previously, it is the current rating (amps) that is critical with 12 volts. Before buying a 12 volt soldering iron check the capacity or output of the power supply that you intend to use to power it.

If you are going to use your controller then it is important that you check the capacity (amps) of the single output you are going to use, not the overall capacity of the controller. It is my experience that most controllers, whilst having a total capacity of 2.5 amps, actually have several outputs, the biggest of which is usually only 1 amp. This could power no more than a 12 watt soldering iron. Anything bigger will need its own separate power supply costing a large amount of money, so it is best to avoid 12 volts for this application.

Wattage

My recommendations are as follows:

N Gauge

Up to 18 watts for all work, with bits up to 4.5mm for trackwork.

25 to 50 watt irons will be required for making models in brass, nickel silver, copper or white metal.

OO Gauge

Up to 25 watts for all work with bits up to 6mm for trackwork.

25 to 70 watt irons will be needed for brass, nickel silver, copper or white metal.

O Gauge

25 to 70 watts for most work with bits up to 12.5mm for trackwork.

Over 100 watts for brass, copper, nickel silver and white metal.

The above recommendations are for average use and some of the sizes can be varied depending on the work to be done. Remember that it is better to have a larger soldering iron with a smaller bit fitted than a small soldering iron with a big bit.

Solder Types

Soldering for model railways will be similar to that of electronics so for most applications the same solders can be recommended. At the same time you should not choose a solder that is too thick, as previously explained.

Suitable sizes are:

N & OO Gauge

Up to 20 swg.

O Gauge

Up to 20 swg for wiring, etc., and up to 16 swg for trackwork.

Fluxes and Tools

An earlier chapter dealt with the different fluxes. For some reason there is a glut of unidentifiable bottles available in the model railway business. Take note of the warnings already given in the flux chapter.

Tools again will be the same as recommended in the electronics section.

Starting to Solder

It should now be obvious that the majority of soldering around a model railway is the same as for electronics and therefore the same technique applies. The main differences will be when soldering to the track or when actually building the models.

Soldering Track

When soldering to the track there are several areas to keep in mind. Firstly, **never** solder on the inside of the track, however tempting this may be. If you do, the train will almost certainly be derailed due to the restriction of the gauge. Secondly, **never** allow the solder to flow onto the top face of the track, this again will cause the train to be derailed. Finally, while British Rail can get away with continuous welded rail, it is totally impractical to do this with model railways. The British Rail technique is to form a weld almost by recasting that part of the joint. If you try to emulate this you will surely fail due to the different expansion factors of the rail and the solder. If you are laying track outdoors, it is wise to use good quality fishplates and then solder wires across the joints on the outsides of the two rails. Then, if oxidisation prevents good electrical conduction across the fishplate, it will be maintained through the wires.

The procedure for soldering to the track is as follows, remembering that a much bigger soldering iron bit will be required due to the mass of metal in the rail:

   (i)   Tin the wires as previously explained.

  (ii)   Apply the soldering iron bit to the outside of the rail and allow the rail to heat up (Figure 10.1).

 (iii)   Apply pre-fluxed solder to the rail, not to the soldering bit. If you do it this way, the solder will only

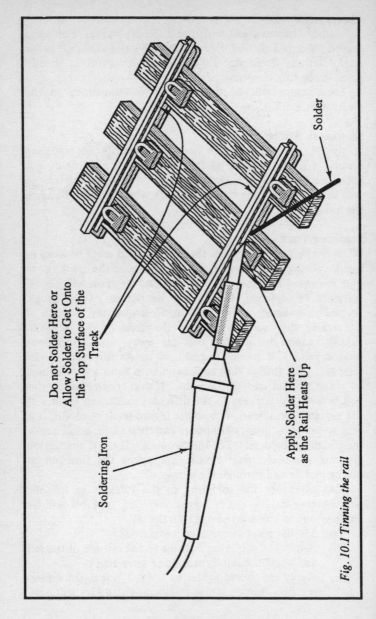

Do not Solder Here or Allow Solder to Get Onto the Top Surface of the Track

Solder

Apply Solder Here as the Rail Heats Up

Soldering Iron

Fig. 10.1 Tinning the rail

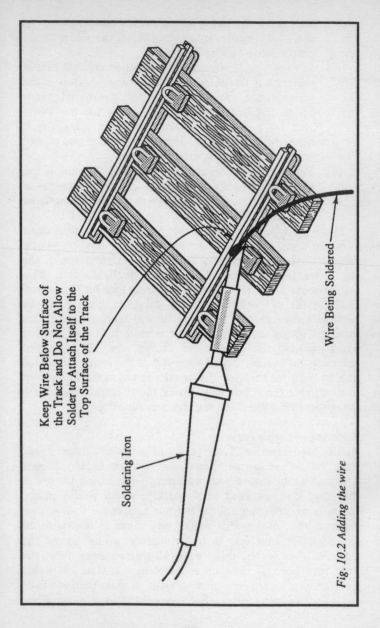

Keep Wire Below Surface of the Track and Do Not Allow Solder to Attach Itself to the Top Surface of the Track

Wire Being Soldered

Soldering Iron

Fig. 10.2 Adding the wire

melt when the rail is at the correct temperature. As previously mentioned, do not allow the solder to get onto the top face of the rail.

(iv) Lay the tinned wire along the tinned rail, but before soldering it to the rail check that the position of the wire will not foul the track. Apply the soldering iron bit to the wire (Figure 10.2) and watch the solder melt on both the wire and the track. This should happen fairly quickly. If it does not then you should be using a bigger soldering iron or bit.

(v) Remove the soldering iron and hold or support the wire very steadily until the solder has hardened, at which time you should have successfully completed the joint.

There are several problems that you may encounter when soldering areas like track. As most track is now on plastic sleepers there is a danger that leaving the soldering iron on the rail for too long will almost certainly melt the sleepers. This will be more likely if you use a soldering iron bit that is too small, as the rail will take much longer to heat up to the required temperature. Secondly, if you use bare solid wire to solder across the track joint, it is more than possible that when soldering the second end of the wire, the first joint will melt and become dry. I suggest that PVC-coated stranded wire be used for bridging the joints. It will not only prevent so much heat travel but will also be more flexible and absorb the obvious vibration from the trains much better.

Soldering of Larger Parts

As has been mentioned several times previously, larger brass, nickel silver and copper parts need a much larger soldering iron and bit to ensure good soldering. The reason for this is that they dissipate heat very quickly, which is why manufacturers of soldering equipment use copper for their soldering iron bits. Whilst this works very much in the favour of the soldering iron bit, it unfortunately works against the modeller due to the heat being dissipated away from the joint very quickly. The other problem is that of joints that have already been made coming apart because the heat from the soldering iron has travelled beyond the work area. When soldering larger items (boilers, frames, coach sides, etc.) it is wise to get them mechanically set up and supported before starting to solder. Even for N Gauge, you will need a fairly large soldering bit for these materials, probably as large as 6mm. You will probably think that this is too large for the area to solder but in my experience anything smaller will cause the inevitable dry joint. Remember that the faster you can complete the joint, the less distance the heat will flow.

The technique for soldering larger areas of these materials is as follows:

(i) Thoroughly clean the areas to be soldered. If possible smooth out any cut or file marks with a fine abrasive like emery cloth, etc. When cleaned, do not touch the areas with your fingers. The grease from your fingers will repel the solder and again cause a dry joint.

(ii) The parts to be soldered should be mechanically set up before soldering, either by wiring them in place or by supporting them in some other way. **I have emphasised previously the heat dissipation factor of these materials. You will probably not be able to hold the parts in place with your fingers long enough for the solder to solidify, due to the heat travel. This will mean that if the joint is not otherwise supported you will inevitably have to let go of the material before the joint is complete to stop burning yourself.**

(iii) Once the areas to be soldered are set up, make sure that the soldering iron can be applied to the joint without difficulty.

(iv) If you need to use additional flux then carefully apply this with a paint brush only where it is needed. Again, all these materials should require only an inert flux. If you use an active flux then you will have to scrub the excess flux off after you have completed the joint.

(v) Apply the soldering iron to the parts to be joined with a bias to the tinned area of the soldering iron bit touching the larger piece of material. Remember that for successful soldering both parts must reach the required temperature.

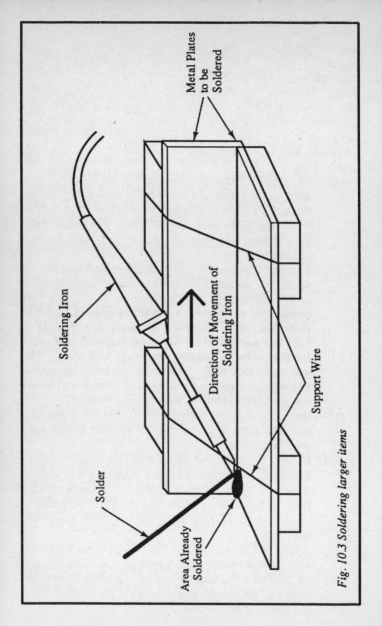

Fig. 10.3 Soldering larger items

(vi) Apply the solder to the material, not the soldering iron bit (Figure 10.3). You should test the area of material slightly away from the joint (approximately 0.5mm) ensuring that the solder melts at that point. Run the solder into the joint and for long runs (e.g. coach sides or boilers) slowly move the soldering iron away from the area already soldered, running the solder after the soldering iron and applying the solder to the material and not the soldering iron. If you have difficulty with this operation then either the soldering iron or the soldering iron bit are not large enough. This means that you will not successfully complete this operation unless you increase the size of one or other item, regardless of the size of the work to be soldered.

(vii) Finish off by removing the soldering iron and running the solder up to the end of the joint.

(viii) Finally, and most importantly, leave the whole area to cool for several minutes. Due to the heat dissipation, a large area of the material will have been heated and will take some time to cool right down.

If you are going to solder several parts together, like for example coach bodies, then these should be pre-assembled and supported to prevent one part falling off when trying to solder another.

Another tip is to use standard solder for the major seams on the larger parts and a lower melting point solder for all the fittings. Remember that no matter how small one of the parts to be soldered may be, it is the larger part that it is most important to get to the right temperature. Obviously, if the same solder that has been used for the main body is used for the fittings, then it is possible to melt the solder on the main body seams. For the same reason, I would not recommend the soldering of white metal parts onto these materials, bearing in mind that, as these materials retain their heat for a long time, it is more than likely that the white metal parts will melt.

Finally, I would reiterate the warning that if you have used active flux, any excess will have to be scrubbed off, so avoid its use if at all possible.

Chapter 11

SOLDERING WHITE METAL

This is probably the most difficult area of any soldering application. One reason is the definition of white metal. Quite simply, it is a term describing castable materials with melting points from approximately 60°C to around 250°C. As can be seen, this immediately presents a problem as to which solder to use. At the extremes the difference in the white metals can be seen by the material's colouration. A blackish appearance will represent a lower melting point, whereas a silvery appearance indicates a higher melting point. Unfortunately, the manufacturers of these kits do not see fit to inform you of the melting point of the material you are supplied with in their instruction leaflets. It is therefore recommended that you contact the manufacturer and get him to supply this very important information before you start to solder, as a different technique will be required for the higher melting point metals to that of the lower ones. It is my experience that the better the quality of the kit then the higher the melting point of the white metal will be.

As most people reading this will be novices at soldering, I would advise that no white metal is soldered using a full temperature soldering iron. This means that you will need a soldering iron controller of some type. Remember the warning earlier in this book regarding the power of 12 volt soldering irons and their requirement for a power supply usually much greater than that available from a normal model railway controller. The most practical solution is a mains controller which enables you to reduce the temperature of the soldering iron. The only other solution is a solder station but these are very expensive.

The type of solder you use will depend on the quality of white metal you are working with. For melting points above 140°C I would recommend a tin/lead/cadmium combination solder with a melting point around 140°C. The cadmium acts as a catalyst and helps the solder to attach itself to the white metal. This type of white metal will be the easiest to solder.

For melting points below 140°C, beware. These will be much more difficult to solder and, unless you are prepared to experiment with a cheap model first, it is most likely that many accidents will occur when soldering. Even with a good quality soldering iron controller, it will be very difficult to keep most irons to a temperature low enough to be safe when soldering this grade of white metal.

Beware also of the "solders" that melt at very low temperatures. Some of these are in fact white metal itself and will in effect be recasting the joint rather than properly soldering it. This will mean actually melting the white metal along the joint to effect the recasting.

Once you have decided which type of white metal you are using, and are prepared to commence soldering, it is advisable to experiment with soldering the odd pieces you find in the kit. If you ruin these then it will not matter. Adjust the temperature of the soldering iron until you can continually solder satisfactorily and get good joints. When you are happy, you can commence with soldering the white metal.

The technique is the same as with all the soldering applications already described and all the areas covered still apply. The correct size of soldering iron and bit are still very important, although the heat will not dissipate through this metal so readily as with brass, copper or nickel silver. This will mean that the heat will tend to be concentrated in a very small area around the soldering iron bit, and will not travel. Therefore, more care must be taken when soldering, especially larger parts, to prevent dry joints.

I still recommend inert fluxes for this material, even though it would be very much easier to solder using an active flux. The problem of continued corrosion of the joint still applies, and unless you can remove the flux completely it will eventually damage your model, as well as the paint you will be applying afterwards.

Chapter 12

SOLDERING AND STAINED GLASS

The use of soldering for stained glass has been going on for many years, but it is only fairly recently that it has grown as a hobby, especially for the construction of terrariums.

Whilst it is possible to use pre-shaped lead strip which you cut to size and then solder together at the joints, the most favoured type of construction involves the use of copper foil strips which are bent around the edges of the glass and then soldered together.

Unfortunately, a large number of these otherwise very attractive items are seriously flawed because of the soldering and the flux that is used.

It is very important to take notice of two factors in this application of soldering:

    (i)   The solder joint must be done quickly to prevent the glass overheating and consequently cracking.

    (ii) The flux used must not corrode away the copper foil, as without this there is nothing left to hold the solder together, thus causing the joint to fall apart.

Unfortunately not enough care is taken in these areas, because most people who attempt this hobby think that soldering is easy. Many a terrarium in the shops is showing the tell-tale green stain along the solder joints. This is the copper foil corroding away because active rather than inert flux has been used, and is therefore continuing to work on the copper foil. Remember that the thickness of copper foil used is probably the same as that on an electronic printed circuit board, and it will therefore be rotted away in a very short time. The likely result when you put your pot plant in the terrarium is that the bottom will fall out.

My recommendations for this type of work are a soldering iron of over 70 watts, fitted with a bit size at least 9.5mm in diameter. The solder should be 60/40 or "Savbit" no thicker than 16 swg, and for a flux, any suitable inert type.

You could test the flux you are going to use by leaving some on the copper foil overnight to see how deep (if not all

71

the way through) it has etched. Again, if you can avoid active fluxes then do so. They should not be necessary and will only spoil your work in the long term.

The technique for soldering with this application is as follows:

(i) Clean the copper foil strip to remove all the grease and dirt from the surface, using a very fine emery cloth or similar.

(ii) Using a pair of **clean** rubber, or similar, gloves place the copper foil around the edges of the glass. Once the copper foil has been cleaned you must not touch it with your fingers. As has previously been mentioned, the grease on your fingers, however often you wash them, will act as a solder repellant.

(iii) Mechanically set up the two (or more) pieces of glass to be soldered.

(iv) Apply the soldering iron bit to the strip you wish to solder, starting at the end furthest away from you. With the front point on the foil, the rear of the soldering iron bit should be slightly off the foil, to allow the solder to be fed in at this point (Figure 12.1).

(v) Apply the solder as above.

(vi) As soon as the solder has melted move the iron towards you, continuing to feed solder under the bit. It should take about 1 minute to complete about a foot of work. Faster than this is good, but if it takes substantially longer then the soldering iron bit is too small.

(vii) Continue soldering the remainder of the work, remembering that you will also have to solder the insides of the joint. If you can get the solder to flow through the crack between the two copper foil edges and attach itself to the solder on the other side then this will give you a much stronger joint.

It would be very wise to keep the whole item solidly physically set up until all soldering work has been completed and all joints have fully hardened before removing it from its support. This will avoid putting strain on any single joint, and will give a much more solid final result.

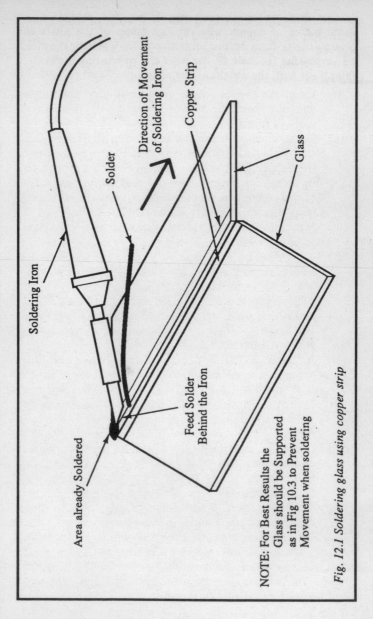

Soldering Iron

Direction of Movement of Soldering Iron

Solder

Copper Strip

Glass

Area already Soldered

Feed Solder Behind the Iron

NOTE: For Best Results the Glass should be Supported as in Fig 10.3 to Prevent Movement when soldering

Fig. 12.1 Soldering glass using copper strip

One final tip with terrariums. If possible, thread one or more pieces of copper wire through some of the joints and around the bottom before soldering. This will have the effect of supporting the base of the item and preventing the bottom falling out with the weight of the plant.

Chapter 13

SOLDERING USING A GAS FLAME

The rules regarding soldering with a gas flame are really the same as with any other equipment. The same requirements apply, especially that of heat, flux and solder. This chapter will deal with soldering larger items such as plumbing, car radiators, etc., including larger locomotive boilers and frames.

When soldering with a gas flame the secret is to bring the area being soldered up to temperature slowly. This is done by moving the flame around the joint and never directing it to just one point. If you do, that point will overheat and burn both the work and the solder which will render the solder useless.

Water and Other Copper Pipes, etc.

The method of soldering all copper pipes will be the same, although the materials to be used, i.e. the solder and the flux, are strictly controlled by the Building Regulations for pipes being used for water. These pipes must only be soldered with lead-free solder and special flux. If in doubt ask at your plumbers' merchant.

   (i)   Firstly clean the joint, usually the end of the pipe, thoroughly using wire wool or similar so that the area going into the joint is bright and shiny.

  (ii)   Apply flux to the two parts.

 (iii)   Insert the pipe into the joint.

 (iv)   Repeat the procedure for all ends of the joint. Remember that when one end of the joint is heated, the other joints will also reach the melting point of solder because the copper is a good conductor of heat.

  (v)   When you are ready to solder, light the flame and adjust it so that it is not a roaring flame. A slightly yellow flame is generally very much better than a roaring blue flame, as you are less likely to overheat a particular part of the joint.

 (vi)   Move the flame slowly up and down the pipe with a bias towards the pipe rather than the joint.

(viii) Remove the flame completely and allow the whole item to cool. Again do not touch, as an area this large will stay hot for a considerable length of time.

(ix) Finally inspect the joint. The solder should be shiny, smooth and even, and should not have sagged, other than very slightly in the centre.

As can be seen the soldering of these larger areas needs a lot of care and attention and you should think carefully before you undertake them. If, for example, you heat the area around the neck of a car radiator to such an extent that the solder around the neck melts then you will be in real trouble. Instead of completing the small repair, you now have a much larger item to repair.

The soldering of all larger items should be undertaken in the same way, with the same care being required. It would help, especially if you are constructing something, if you could get the joints to fix together physically before soldering, so that the solder acts as a filler rather than entrusting the whole seam to the strength of the solder.

Chapter 14

CONCLUSION

I hope that I have demonstrated that soldering is not difficult, but is more difficult to do properly. Great care must be taken with all stages of soldering and the slightest omission could cause a bad joint.

To sum up the main points of soldering which must be correct:

   (i) **CLEANLINESS** – If the joint is clean you will get good results.

  (ii) **THE CORRECT SIZE OF SOLDERING IRON.**

 (iii) **THE CORRECT FLUX.**

 (iv) **THE CORRECT SIZE OF SOLDER.**

Get all these items correct and dry joints will be a thing of the past.

Notes

Please note following is a list of other titles that are available in our range of Radio, Electronics and Computer books.

These should be available from all good Booksellers, Radio Component Dealers and Mail Order Companies.

However, should you experience difficulty in obtaining any title in your area, then please write directly to the Publisher enclosing payment to cover the cost of the book plus adequate postage.

If you would like a complete catalogue of our entire range of Radio, Electronics and Computer Books then please send a Stamped Addressed Envelope to:

BERNARD BABANI (publishing) LTD
THE GRAMPIANS
SHEPHERDS BUSH ROAD
LONDON W6 7NF
ENGLAND